Breaking Cover – 2

An Anthology of Country Tales

by Jackie Drakeford

Published in 2013 by Skycat Publications
Vaiseys Farm, Brent Eleigh, Suffolk CO10 9 PA
Email info@skycatpublications.com
www.skycatpublications.com

ISBN 978-0-9567029-7-5

Printed by Lavenham Press
Arbons House, 47 Water Street, Lavenham, Suffolk CO10 9RN
Telephone: +44 (0)1787 247436
Email: enquiries@lavenhamgroup.co.uk

Acknowledgements

Some of the articles in this collection are previously unpublished, while versions of the others have previously appeared in *Shooting Times, Countryman's Weekly* or *Sporting Shooter*, for which thanks are extended to the editors involved.

Photographs remain copyright of the author, except where otherwise indicated. Thanks are due to F. Sechiari for allowing the use of her photographs. Edward Andrews has kindly allowed the reproduction of his artwork on page 131. Guest articles on page 119 and 125 are copyright of Phillip Blackman. Back cover image also courtesy of F. Sechiari.

Other titles by the same author

Breaking Cover -1
published 2013

The Working Lurcher - The Traditional Skills
published 2006

The House Lurcher
first published 2003, second edition 2010

Rabbit Control
first published 2002, revised edition 2008

Understanding the Working Lurcher
published 2000

Working Ferrets
published 1996, second edition 2011

Essential Care in the Field
co-authored with Mark Elliott M.R.C.V.S.
first published 2007
will be revised 2013 by Skycat publications

Essential Care for Dogs
co-authored with Mark Elliott M.R.C.V.S.
published 2005

About the author

The author is well-known for her books and articles on country sports and working dogs, which appear regularly in a variety of fieldsports publications. Now living in rural Sussex, she grew up in the New Forest, where the Game Laws have been a thorn in the flesh of the locals ever since William the Conqueror came over and started acting as if he owned the place. Horses, hounds, lurchers, terriers and ferrets have figured largely in her life from an early age, and she has a deep respect and appreciation of the wild creatures that pepper her tales.

Jackie is a Kennel Club Accredited Instructor and dog behaviour trainer, working with an integrated veterinary practice as well as writing articles and lecturing on dog behaviour.

Contents

X

Introduction

Here in this second collection of countryside tales, we meet old friends and find some new ones too, as we accompany the author out with her dogs and at the mercy of those rustic surprises that can catch any of us unawares. This is real countryside, wet, muddy and overgrown, where Triumph and Disaster are easy companions. We all know how quickly one can change to the other before the human side of the arrangement has time to get on terms - and by then, the dogs are there already. Ah yes, the dogs: the lurchers and terriers, hounds and gundogs that sweep us up with the scent into their thought processes, and take us where we are so privileged to be. Dry, laconic, brief and to the point, the author takes us across the land by day and by night, and shares those times in the field that are oh so familiar to grassroots sportsmen and women.

Once more we have two guest contributions from her stoical ever-supportive partner, who provides a highly individual, heavily biased view from the beating line, especially where terriers are concerned.

Some of the incidents described in the following pages took place before the Hunting Act, and some afterwards. The discerning reader will know which are which.

One

Some Chickens

IT was some considerable time ago that I agreed to help out the friend of a friend who had to be away at short notice. He had a number of working dogs and 'some chickens' to be cared for. His home was a converted stable block on an estate where the 'big house' had long since fallen to ruin, and the conversion had been made long before Health and Safety had ever been thought about. "You'll never find it" he told me, "I'll meet you at the Crown and lead you in".

He was right - I would never have found it. Parking by the well in the cobbled courtyard, I heard a commotion and saw a wirehaired dachshund scooting out of a shed. There was a lean buff-brown chicken attached to her rump by its feet, pecking her vigorously and flapping to keep its balance. "Falconry" said the man, with a quiet smile. The dog dived under a low piece of wood, and the fowl fell off.

What a bird! I had never seen such economy of build, such tightness of plumage. Tall, compact, balanced like a prizefighter, muscled like a racehorse, nothing too much, nothing lacking. Her feathers fitted her like a lizard's scales, but with the shine of chain mail. She caught my eye with the glare of a basilisk, the creature born of a cockerel's egg, but if I were temporarily turned to stone, it was purely in admiration

of her looks. Then she roused her feathers and strolled back to the shed, and, as I discovered later, her nest.

There were several arrangements of poultry: some wandered free-range, day and night, and made their roost wherever they chose, whether in the beams of one of the outbuildings or in one of the trees surrounding. Some were contained in runs, always a cockerel and a harem of hens. Some were broods with partridge-coloured chicks. I was to feed and water, pick up eggs, let out and shut in some, but keep others confined always. It sounded easier than it was.

Collecting the long white eggs from under hens that had other plans for them was a hazardous task, and my knuckles were slashed on the first day from one of those sledgehammer pecks. I needed those eggs: I could catch rabbits on the estate, take what I wanted from the overgrown cottage garden and eat freely of the eggs, but those were my only food sources. I took a saucepan and covered the head of each hen while I

stole from her, but even so, sometimes one would throw off her mask and savage me: they would bite and hold on like ferrets. Then there were the escapes: those fowl which must not be let out of their run would be through the smallest gap as I went in to feed and water, and then I had to wait until dusk to round them up again, carrying them, screaming and spinning like dervishes, back to their pens. They bit me as well, beat me with their wings, scratched long grooves down me, given the chance. I learned to pick a sumptuous bouquet of greenstuff and put it in the furthermost corner of the pen before I opened the gate; sometimes humans have the edge on intellect, if not athleticism. Fortunately there were plenty

of desirable plants: chickweed, grass, dandelions, groundsel and of course the herb called fat hen. After a few days, they raced me to the far corner when they saw me carrying their greenery, and my gate problems were at an end even if the egg issues continued. Around the field perimeter prowled the free cockerels, occasionally skirmishing or holding a crowing match, but nothing serious because they were young and there was plenty of space. "Black Reds" he had called them.

I soon had my routine established where an early start and a frantic round of exercising dogs, cleaning kennels, chopping wood, feeding and watering, and collecting eggs (ouch) led to a leisurely al fresco lunch at a rickety table on the cobbles outside the kitchen. Here I would be joined by Dennis, my favourite cockerel. He would sit on the top of the back door and talk poultry talk to me. He was not after food, and seldom deigned to investigate the crumbs I would throw. For some reason, Dennis liked human company, and I rather liked his. As the sun became too hot for anything except dozing, Dennis and I would slump companionably together, me in the chair and him on the door, unless he found a sunny patch at my feet, where he would sprawl like a broken umbrella, one wing out to the side, catching the rays.

After an agreeable siesta, Dennis would return to whatever it is cockerels have to do, and I would start the work round again. Then the dogs and I would go on fox patrol as the interested indeed, and though normally a silent dog, found it necessary to comment. There really were rather a lot of deer.

One then ran straight up to us, lost its footing and went hooves up right at my feet. The lurcher could have caught it with slack in her lead, and didn't she create as I dragged her away. I think that's the nearest that dog has ever come to biting me, and she sulked for days afterwards. I also remember when she was just learning to lamp, and we were on a knife-edge of control. I had a hundred and sixty acres to play in that night, and there was hardly a rabbit to be seen. Finally I saw the perfect sitter, lots of field around it and slightly uphill from us. Hearts pounding, we crept up on this rabbit. The dog was sighted just right, and I slipped her as it leapt up and started to run. Beautiful. Then, to my utter dry-mouthed horror, between the fleeing rabbit and the pelting dog lumbered a large grey shape. The fawn bitch swung off the small quarry onto the large one, and the next few seconds went into slow-motion.

I'd taught her to come back when I switched off the lamp. I switched off the lamp and she didn't come back.

I'd taught her to leave when I shouted 'Leave' so I did that and she didn't leave it.

I thought I'd better switch the lamp back on to see what was happening, and realised I hadn't known badgers could run that fast. I hadn't realised I could, either. Luckily she was a clever bitch despite her youth, so when she picked it up by its tail and it swiped at her, she dropped it, and I finally caught up and sorted things out. The badger escaped unhurt into the dark, where it carried on foraging, quite unruffled, the dog was very ruffled indeed and prepared for a marathon sulking session, any rabbits still left above ground on the farm now weren't, and I very nearly needed counselling.

You can even have oh-no-seconds with small quarry like rabbits and squirrels, especially if it is summer and you are out without pockets, which is why I always wear a waistcoat these days no matter how hot it might be. There are so many occasions when it has proved handy, such as the time the Bedlington Thing chased a squirrel across the churchyard.

Well yes, he should have been on a lead, but he always walked nicely to heel, and in common with most working dogs was better behaved off-lead than most pet dogs are when on one. But a squirrel sitting on a gravestone just has to be chased; it ran up the side of the church, and so did he, the knapped flint just giving enough grip. He caught it too, right by one of the stained-glass windows, and then looked at me for help "what happens now?"

"You fall off", I replied, and he did, but he never let go of the squirrel. I managed to stuff its corpse in my pocket just as some people arrived to change the flowers on a grave (nothing ever got out of his mouth alive) and the departing fleas weren't much more of a problem than normal.

One day, the Bedlington Thing gave the Sahib a special treat. It was during the time I was laid up, and so he was walking the dogs on his own. The little lurcher caught a

squirrel and retrieved it, but when the Sahib went to take it from him, he flashed his slanting amber eyes and said, "Not likely - this is for the Boss". So the poor man had to walk along a well-used public footpath accompanied by a likely-looking bunch of mutts, one of which was wearing a squirrel like a Cossack moustache. He carried it up the path, through the door, jumped onto my bed and lovingly presented me with it.

I must say, it was absolutely delicious. Well actually, a swift sleight of hand meant that it was hidden to one side while I made a great fuss of my clever little dog. The ferrets got the squirrel, which they said was absolutely delicious, and the Bedlington Thing never knew. It must have been one of the longest retrieves ever, especially when you realise he carried it all the way home, sitting up in the passenger seat of the car holding onto his squirrel.

Three

As Others See Us

WE who keep long spiky dogs tend to think that ours are the norm and it's the others that barely qualify as dogs, but the rest of the world finds them strange, and doesn't hesitate to comment. Over the years I have had some very odd remarks made to me, and though I am seldom lost for words, the replies that spring to my lips are usually better kept in check. After all, people do not mean to offend, or else come across as total numpties, do they?

You and I get used to being told how thin our dogs are, with varying degrees of intent, from the person who thinks they are cruelty cases and is going to "report" us, to the chap with two rotund whippets on extending leads that I met this week. "Your dogs must run around a lot," he said, and I agreed that they did. "These just sit on the sofa and eat", he explained. You can struggle for an answer to that. I am used to being told that my dogs "only need two twenty-minute walks a day", well, yes, you could say that as they probably run for the rest of the time, and that they are "easy to train" which last punctured my balloon decisively as I thought they were being rather good at the time, in the face of severe provocation. One woman (with a mega fat Jack Russell) asked me how I stopped them from "running off" and when I said "with a fence" she sneered so hard her nose nearly knotted itself. "You have to fence them in?". Tish. What a useless owner I am. Maybe I should just feed them until they can't move.

Quite a few people comment that they didn't know greyhounds had rough coats too, and I regret my naughty brother told one lady, in a cod Irish accent, "We shave dem for de racin' so we do" at which she nodded wisely, having just remembered that of course we did. Only last week an elderly man asked politely if they were "young wolves" which delighted them so that they pranced all the way home ("we're wolves! We're well'ard!"). The wolf thing also came up a couple of years ago when I was walking through the woods rather early, dogs questing in front, and heard an almighty series of screams. I found two early-teens campers who looked as if they had seen a ghost. "We thought they was wolfs", said one. It's sweet really.

I am often told that my dogs should not be offlead "because
you can't get them back when they run off, can you?" or that
they should be wearing muzzles (so should you, sir). People
have the idea that lurchers spend all their time chasing cats,
and cannot comprehend that it is possible to train a dog not to,
and they wonder that our chickens remain unmolested. What
would they say if they saw one of the black hens fluffled down
in front of the fire in the winter, sharing the hearthrug with
these savage dogs? I don't like hens in the house, but these
have learned to use the dogs as stalking horses, sneaking in
among the forest of legs and remaining undetected until they
cluck.

Quite a few people think that lurchers "tear rabbits to
pieces" and I have known one or two that did, but not any of
mine. They are politely disbelieving when I mention the "live
to hand" requirement, and treat themselves to a patronising
smirk. Of course, any dog that has ever "chased and killed"
could never be a household pet, one professional dog trainer
told a friend of mine.

Sometimes people that you thought were quite intelligent
come out with an absolute Brahma, and this happened
recently - in fact I am still having therapy. This very nice
woman with whom I often exchange the time of day when

ground-nesting birds of the rare variety (much appreciated by the corvids and foxes but we didn't touch on this) and outlined what the farmer had been doing in this, his first year of farming wildlife. The fence stopped uncontrolled dogs from harassing the birds and was therefore a Good Thing (it had left certain of us with rather moist fireworks, but you could see the farmer's point). All the time walking away from where I could hear the high-pitched accelerating yip of a terrier hot on the heels of whatever it was, we discussed the wide variety of birds around us, and parted, I like to think, on amiable terms.

I left them at the junction of footpaths, having confirmed which was the one they should be following, and was about

to return to the job in hand when the Bedlington Thing appeared over the rife in front of them and ran towards me with something floppy in his mouth.

*Sussex drainage ditch

Five

Rescue on the Hill

THE great thing about complacency is that you only realise you had some when you are most uncomfortably jolted out of it. I fielded averagely good ferrets, hunting with them all year round. They were very friendly and easy to handle, got a light breakfast before we set off, and didn't lie up. If a rabbit wouldn't bolt, it was either dragged out or killed and left. I actually went years without ever having a ferret lie up (I've made up for that many times since) and the first time it ever happened was one I shall remember for ever.

Shortly after daybreak on a drizzly Saturday morning, I put two jills into a hillside bury that had, thanks to an exceptionally dry summer, been grazed clear of its protective nettles by the sheep, who had little else to eat. A stunted hazel bush leaned against a slightly less stunted ash, and the rest of the bury was clear. For a while, the usual sorts of things happened, after which the white jill came out and indicated that she had finished, but there was no sign of the silvermitt jill, who was a particular favourite of mine.

The Sahib returned from netting up an adjacent bury, and the lurcher arrived from the opposite direction (how is it they do that?) with a live rabbit that had been watching us from what it had presumed was a safe place. We sent the white jill underground again, and she came straight back. "Nuthin' doing down there, Boss," she said. That's also what the locator said: absolutely nothin'.

I'd put new batteries into an almost new collar and was getting no reading. Could be the cap had worked loose, could be my rather old and often dropped receiver box had given up working, could be that she was so far down that she was out of range, which isn't difficult on a hillside. I've come in for a bit of flak here and there because I like to use fifteen foot collars, the argument being (quite correctly) that I'm not going to dig fifteen feet. Indeed I'm not, but I like to know where my ferret is, and whether she is moving or still. Today there was no reading; not a peep.

Knowing that if my ferrets can come out they always will, I sat by the bury to wait while the Sahib ferreted the other bury and the lurcher brought me another rabbit from who knows where. She was supposed to be assisting at the other bury but was clearly suffering a conflict of loyalties which was most easily solved by catching rabbits that were hiding in cover and bringing them to me. Still no ferret and no reading.

Once the white jill had cleared the second bury, we sent her through this one again, but no luck. "I don't know why you keep doing that", she said, "There's nothing in there". The Sahib went home, half an hour's drive away once he had walked down the hill to the track, and fetched the larger of our two vasectomised hob ferrets, the one that lived full-time with this pair of jills. Collared up, batteries checked and working, he waddled purposefully under, and we tracked his progress all through the bury until - praise be - we picked up a second signal. Out came the hob. This wasn't what was supposed to happen, so we put him in again, telling him to fetch his wife out or else. The signal was at four feet, but with the whole bury to choose from (this won't surprise any ferreter) was at the roots of the ash tree. The ferret had not moved and she did not move. The options as we saw them were: laid up and eating, laid up and sleeping, hung up on a root by her collar, trapped down a vertical shaft, trapped by the body of a rabbit, injured, unconscious or dead.

24

The place was undiggable for us, equipped as we were for a simple day's ferreting. Two sets of tree roots plus (as it turned out) the trunk of another tree just below the surface was too much for the graft, and night was upon us. Sadly, we left a ferret box with some liver in it by the closest rabbit hole, and went home, stopping only to tell the gamekeeper whose beat our permission was on.

First light the next day it was hissing down with rain, nobody was in the ferret box, and the signal was the same at four feet. The slope was dangerous in these conditions, and there was nothing more we could do. We went home, made some tea, watched it go cold and then the phone rang. This is when you find out who your friends are.

The 'keeper and his wife piled us into his Landrover, which was already laden with an arsenal of serious digging gear.

He drove up the slope as far as was safe, then a bit further, and then we got out and walked. A stiff breeze began to lift the clouds high enough to stop the rain as we struggled up the slippery incline, and the reading was steady at four feet. "Stupid place to put a couple of trees", he said, "right in the middle of a rabbit bury", and he started to dig.

This was a man who had dug to a tidy few foxes, and his experience showed in an exquisite economy of effort. The dead tree was broken up and extracted; the living trees had their toenails delicately pared with consideration to doing the least possible damage. At three feet, he struck chalk, and still he dug, the Sahib shovelling out the debris as they went. The reading began to fluctuate, but we all know that these tiny transmitters could be unreliable in the wet, and this one had been going for almost thirty hours.

"I can hear scratching", said the 'keeper.

"I can see a root moving", said his wife.

A tiny rootlet was quivering. Carefully the chalk and soil was scraped away from around it, and a tiny pink nose appeared. The ferret, which had never been dug to in her life, was digging towards the sound of rescue. She had, we found, been trapped between the body of a rabbit she had killed and a mesh of tree roots, against a wall of chalk. She was very

pleased to see us, very thirsty, and her neck had been rubbed raw by the collar, so she had possibly been caught up at some stage as well. Otherwise she was fine and we made a great fuss of her.

Ridiculous how attached you get to a few ounces of animated fluff, isn't it? We went back and celebrated with coffee and biscuits, the ferret sitting in state on the kitchen worktop and quaffing a saucer of milk. The gamekeeper waved away our thanks with a "Couldn't leave a little ferret trapped underground, could we?" and went off to pamper his pheasants. We took a tired and very lucky ferret back home.

She sniffed the dead rabbit that was the day's rations, and said, "I'm sick of rabbit - haven't you got a nice crow?"

Six

Evensong

ITHINK we working dog chaps all know how important it is not to exercise a dog that has just been fed, so let me tell you about the time I nearly blew it.

It was a balmy summer evening, and I still had the horse then, living out his retirement at a place close enough to walk to. The lurchers and I would stroll down at dusk, they to sniff around and have a last wee and testament before bed, and I to check the old lad over. This particular evening, the Sahib decided to join me, bringing his two terriers, all the dogs having been fed not long previously. Duties completed, we were just leaving when a fox strolled across the yard.

There was a certain amount of wheelspin. A russet blur led two lurchers into the field, followed by the young terrier going so fast I couldn't see her legs. I ran round the corner to see her engaged in a revolting personal matter on the verge, and while I was wondering how she could be in two places at once, eyesight caught up with thought and I realised it was the geriatric old Lakeland that was in fact right behind the lurchers - in those days I was fielding a brace of Deerhound crosses, and they had some pace on them. The horse knew a bit about foxhunting, and stuck his tail in the air, shook his old legs into a gallop and shed twenty years as he hammered down the field towards the church wall. I could foresee

mayhem if he jumped it, and he was perfectly capable, but luckily he swerved at the last minute, sending the fox back towards the lurchers, who twanged through three strands of barbed wire with the Lakeland still only just off the pace. By then, the young terrier had finished her project and was hacking down the field in their wake, and it had all happened so quickly that I was still inhaling to call them back - fat chance now they were all launched. The dogs went out of sight into the grounds of a big posh house, and the horse pelted back towards me, swerved broadside, ducked, and told me to get on board sharpish, we'd soon catch them up. I declined, and so he thundered back up the field and started patrolling the place where the dogs had gone through, while I prayed he wouldn't tackle the barbed wire.

At length, the ancient Lakeland toddled back into view, batteries flat, once more her doddery senile old self. Then the senior lurcher cantered back, waving her tail. There was a longish pause, long enough for me to get really worried, and the younger lurcher reappeared and slid through the fence, looking considerably thinner and soaking wet. She had evidently barfed her supper up on the immaculate lawn,

to its owner in a steaming, panting heap, only too grateful to sit at their feet, while the Black Death does a lap of honour around most of the field.

Has woofums got too much energy? Let it run about with BD for ten minutes, and then it will be desperate to walk quietly at heel. Mind you, even she came close to pleading for mercy the day her morning walk involved consecutively two cockers, a springer, a brace of flatcoats, one Labrador, and then we saw the Irish setter. Unusually for Irish setters, this one is beautifully under control, but she loves a game of chase. The Black Death was a shadow of her former self by the time we finished that one, luckily close to the stream where she could have a good wallow in the radioactive mud.

Another useful training aid is the crow. All my dogs have caught one or two crows in a lifetime, either 'branchers' that have fallen off, or sickly adults, because a dog would be a marvel if it could catch a healthy crow. I don't like them catching crows because of the damage that pickaxe beak can do to shiny lurcher eyes, but chasing crows is another matter. Crows play with dogs, staying on the ground until the last minute and then flapping gleefully off about four feet high, while the dog runs after. Just how fast can a crow fly? They seem to lob along in such a leisurely fashion, while a lurcher that you know can cruise at 30mph is putting it all in, never getting closer, never losing ground, until the crow gives a couple of lazy flaps and soars into the sky.

Then there is a cloud of dust growing larger as it comes towards you, a big lurcher grin at its centre, and all whirling tail and skidding limbs as your dog decelerates dramatically beside you. If a mud wallow is followed by a crow course on newly-drilled ground, the dog returns looking like a scotch egg, but I find most of the grot comes off on the furniture later. Maybe if you took a crow young enough, you could train it. Coursing the carted crow - now there is a sport for the future.

Eight

One More Trip

IT happens every year. Just as the ferreting is pretty much over, people start looking out of the window and seeing rabbits. As a courtesy, and because permission is always hard to get and you can never have too much of it, I go and have a look. Sometimes I can actually do something to help, despite the baby rabbits and nettles, so there is the odd end-of-season foray, more protocol than pest control, but we do our best.

Which is why I was trying to net buries in old woodland that hadn't been maintained since Noah collected wood from here for the prototype Ark, and the Sahib was hacking down big healthy brambles ahead of me when he'd rather have been doing almost anything else. The nettles had grown at least an inch since the previous day when I'd checked to see if the buries were ferretable, and the rabbit holes were full of brittle pieces of tree and dead leaves. But the dog marked, and looked at us with glowing eyes, and she never lies.

Swearing like a sailor, I picked brash from the nets I dropped, or were plucked from the bury by mischievous thorned branches that raked across me for an encore, lost my footing down hidden pop-holes (it's one way to find them) and explored the stinging power of nettles barely old enough to be out of nappies. I worked my way along, bury by bury, netting the more accessible holes, while the Sahib furtled about in the thickets, netting those places you always get a bolt from, in the middle of the thorns. We set around three hundred purse nets: if you tried to longnet this, you'd lose hole-hoppers and probably still be picking out debris now. I was hoping to show these very nice landowners that we could do a worthwhile job, especially as they disliked dogs in general and lurchers in particular, because of bad experiences in the past. No pressure, then.

We started at the draughtier end of the wood, expecting that rabbit numbers would increase as we reached the more sheltered buries. This worked as predicted, and we bolted about one rabbit every ten minutes which, given the difficulty of crossing the ground, and the tangle power of all the dead wood and leaves on the buries, was about as fast as we needed. At one stage, the dog dived under a half-fallen tree to hold a netted rabbit, the Sahib vaulted over the trunk in a rush of

Photo: Fay Sechiari.

adrenaline, and the tree was a lot more rotten than it looked. It shattered in a shower of branches, dust and splinters to fall around the poor dog, who was luckily unhurt and what's more, she didn't let go of the rabbit.

Meanwhile, I was trying to deal with the kind of buck rabbit that has a personal trainer, or maybe is one. So strong were its abs that it was curving upwards to snap at me, and I had the devil of a job to despatch it without getting bitten. When we reached the first bury in the newly-customised thorn thicket, rabbits really started bolting: at one stage the Sahib and I were holding two each and the dog had one. I was having a bit of a struggle with mine, being straddled with each foot down a rabbit hole to prevent anything bolting before I had re-netted, two netted rabbits to kill and untangle, and a ferret climbing up my leg. The Sahib was being a bit slow in noticing, so after he had helped the dog with hers, I regret I reverted to type.

"Excuse me", I said apologetically and in cut-crystal tones, "Please would you give me a hand with this lot?" We do polite ferreting here, apart from the foul language incurred by the netting procedure earlier. It's okay as long as you don't drop your aitches.

Given the lateness of the season and the cold wind, we were really pleased with the obliging way that the rabbits were bolting, but the ferrets were spending a lot of time and energy chasing rabbit kittens, which after the first lie-up depleted our mustelid team by one, as she was full-fed and sleepy. Mine don't usually eat rabbit kits while working, but these must have been extra delicious, because we had two more lie-ups for the same reason, and the last hole the Sahib had to dig (he gets all the good jobs) was rather deep. The ground was difficult, being a thin layer of soil over gravel and shale, and of course there were tree roots for variety. Fortunately we were nearly at the end of the netted buries by then, so agreed that it was a good time to stop. Picking up that many nets is quicker than setting them but still takes a while and by the

time the rabbits had been paunched out as well it was another hour gone. The wind was getting up and rain threatened, so we had done well for the time. The dog had played an absolute blinder: at eight years old and even with the niggling injuries that go with being a working dog for that length of time, she was responsible for almost all our catches because she pinned the rabbits in the nets and stopped them escaping when the mesh tangled in the woodland debris. Moreover, she is an ambassador for lurchers, and had sold herself so well when I first met the landowners that they were no longer opposed to having her there.

As for the ferrets, they have maybe one more season in them before a couple of years of well-deserved retirement, and I had seriously been thinking about giving up ferreting as well, because the ground gets ever further away and harder to cross, equipment gets heavier, and everything hurts more afterwards. However, I had so enjoyed the last few trips of the season, including this one, that I have decided to get a couple of kits this year from my usual supplier, and carry on.

Nine

The Sea Rabbit

IF you want to explore the science of what cannot possibly happen but just did, try owning a lurcher. Consider a friend of mine, who saw her sapling lurcher run up behind an angler, steal the fish he had just caught and put on the bank - thankfully without the hook in - and retrieve it to her. When she was a bit slow in taking it, he swallowed it. Well, you can't waste them. I remember the Worm finding a caught fish on the bank, whipping round with the speed of light and piddling on it with dainty accuracy. At times like this I can move surprisingly quickly.

Then there was the hare that bounced out of some sand dunes with a brace of lurchers after it, and when the owner of these fine hounds topped the rise, he saw the course going on in the midst of around a hundred people ready to start a fishing match. Fortunately, the hare went back to the dunes and thence to ground, (oh yes they do) allowing for the "keep your head down and keep walking" departure technique, for fisherfolk are sensitive and can be easily offended. Though not, it has to be said, as touchy as a gamekeeper who has just had one of his hares retrieved to him by a lurcher he had never met before in his life.

Many of my lurcher-related surprises involve the pursuit of a quarry species in front of an unsympathetic audience. One Christmas, for instance, saw us exercising the dogs on the beach, right down by the lowest point of the tide, which was just turning. We were nearly at the pier, having strolled for a pleasant couple of miles along the sand, when, I kid you not, a rabbit dashed out of a patch of seaweed that was already being washed by the incoming waves. A big fat buck rabbit in good health for the last time in its life, three hundred yards from the dunes on a beach that had scores of people and dogs walking along it, and it had to get up in front of two lurchers.

Had it just swum across from France? Been dropped by a clumsy eagle? Did the dune rabbits come down every night to eat seaweed, and this one had fallen asleep? Had he been following the tide out and been caught when it turned? Was this a speeded-up example of lagomorph evolution? A rabbit stag-night prank? Was he depressed? We shall never know.

What I do know is that he died in front of a large audience, and this is a reminder that you should always carry poo bags big enough to hold a rabbit, for no conjurer concealed a rabbit faster than I hid that one. The coastguard helicopter went

back home to change dogs. The lady caller had wandered innocently into her dining room to find a ferret curled up on her son's discarded football kit (Ah! Those pheromones!) Her early morning screams and rapid doorslamming retreat had roused the rest of the household, and after the resultant melee of scantily-clad husband and teenagers had died down, the ferret (which had done a runner) was found again, this time snuggled up against an accommodating Labrador. This Labrador is such a thoroughly nice dog that she just sniffed her new pet ferret, licked it, and went back to sleep. There was a unanimous vote to call on us, as they knew we had ferrets and ...

I passed on the address of the other ferret owner, lent her a carrying box and offered to catch the ferret, but she said she thought her husband could cope, as she had left him cooing at it and offering it dog food on a spoon. Away she went, and I set out with the second shift of dogs.

Arriving back just over an hour later, I was greeted by the same lady returning my empty ferret carrier. She had, she reported with some glee, managed to get a total of four half-naked men out of bed, reunited the ferret with its owner, who had now found his other ferret as well, gone in to see her daughter's Headmaster as it was likely that a mere note about a ferret in the dining room causing lateness might not quite cut the mustard, and was now going to work. Only the Labrador appeared a bit put out at losing her new pet.

Anyway, what I am saying here is: please check the security of your ferret hutches because we don't want any more ferrets no matter how cute they are or what kind of trouble you are in, and we really would like an early night. Thanks.

Eleven

Night Sights

IDON'T know which is more fun: starting a young dog lamping or going out with your trained dog, making it all look easy. Of course everything has its frustrations: the sassy young dog that has been out twice and thinks it knows everything (Why should I come straight back? Look, there's another one – and another – there's loads of them out here) blasting round the field putting everything to ground, or the older dog with a twinge or two, working its last season, where you try to pick out easy rabbits and they all turn out to be on rocket-fuel.

Worst of all is leaving the old dog at home, burning holes in you with its eyes because it knows exactly what is going on even though you hid the lamp in the car hours before. But once you are out there, the day drops from your shoulders, and you bliss into glorious anticipation mingled with the scents of the night.

You see some amazing sights. I can remember a 4WD full of people careering round my permission, blasting away with shotguns, totally unknown to the farmer. Turned out it was a group of police cadets in the charge of the contractor, who had evidently suffered a memory lapse over the niceties of land ownership. The farmer was incandescent, but we had a jolly revenge as I was also part-time farm secretary there, and I really enjoyed writing the various letters.

One night, a tall figure with a gun loomed suddenly out of just-forming mist, making the dog push, growling, into my legs. We crept around the back and got quite close in before I realised it was a scarecrow. That sort of thing does test your deodorant somewhat. But the sight that nearly did for me was once when the lamp lit up this huge, ghastly grinning head moving slowly about at ground level. At times like this, no matter how worldly you are in daylight, the primitive brain takes over with a surge of pure distilled terror. People really shouldn't send those charity balloons out, you know, they could give someone a heart attack.

I recall taking someone out lamping for the first time, after a severe briefing on not making unnecessary noise, and noticing that he was causing a certain amount of pollution as well. It turned out that he had not been feeling too well, but was so excited at the thought of going lamping that he wasn't intending to miss it for a touch of bellyache. We were not on

that the rabbits refused to bolt, so the ferrets herded them into stop-ends and stayed with them. Balanced delicately on a crumb of earth, Paul began to wield the graft, and Sam started to dig a hole of his own. Various people told me that we should get at least thirty rabbits out, and the fawn bitch, who has Standards, began to sulk.

Time passed. Sometimes Paul would haul a bedraggled rabbit out of a hole and pass it to me to neck, his other limbs being totally occupied with staying attached to the side of the rife. Sometimes a rabbit would stick its head out of a rabbit-hole and be met with pointing and cries of delight from our various observers, which for some reason would make it change its mind about bolting. Crawling painfully into the blackthorn, I struggled to reach our only netted rabbit so far, and came face to face with Paul, who couldn't reach it either. The slavering jaws of the collie then blocked both our views, and even he couldn't reach the rabbit. It reversed delicately out of the net and went back underground, pulling the net into a useless heap in the process. As it did so, Paul made a lunge at another rabbit and an awful splash followed. Despite his length, strength and agility, he disappeared into the black water and proved that, yes, tall as he was, it came all the way up to his waist. I have never heard Paul swear before.

Finally, the ferrets gave up and came out; once we had them safely back in custody (one family member having appropriated the ferret box to sit on) we counted eight rabbits caught so far, seven of which had been dug out with no thanks to me. Meanwhile, a Mum had arrived with a picnic and a few more people, which kept the numbers up as some of our original observers had got bored and drifted away, disappointed by the lack of action. Paul emerged from his attempt to walk on water, looking like the Swamp Monster and smelling very organic. He briefly considered removing his jeans, thought better of it, and settled for emptying his boots and wringing out his socks instead. Accepting a warming cup of coffee, he gradually returned almost to his normal colour, and when asked by the audience, offered the observation that the water was indeed very cold.

I though eight rabbits was a pretty good catch given the circumstances, but our watchers were unimpressed because surely there was at least another 22 left there. The lad was told to show us another bury (they really didn't understand why we couldn't do this one over again and get the missing rabbits) so we picked up the gear and started walking, Paul's wet wellies squeaking and flubbering with every step. At times like this, I think it a pity that the dogs can't carry a few nets or something, as they dash merrily around while we plod and try not to gasp. We moved steadily uphill, with considerable difficulty in my case, and paused only to scale a high rickety gate which was leaning at a murderous angle. We were almost at the top of the rise when the lad told us that there was no way through the hedge, and so we trudged down again like the troops of the grand old Duke of York, scaled the same gate that was even more difficult that way round, over a more wobbly gate that wasn't so high, and back up the same hill but further along. Well, it beats the hell out of going to the gym I suppose. Paul never said one word about how cold, wet and generally uncomfortable he must have been feeling, the fawn bitch sulked a black cloud, the collie was eternally frisky as collies are, and I needed chocolate and oxygen, maybe not in that order.

Finally, we reached another part of the rife, this one gloriously free from blackthorn and packed both sides with rabbit-holes. The opposite side especially, which wasn't ours to ferret as it was someone else's land. Feeling pretty jaded, and as time was now getting on, we decided not to net the holes this time (could have saved carrying the net bag up two hills, couldn't we?) but simply to bolt rabbits for the dogs to catch. Within seconds of the first ferret entering, a rabbit shot out of an adjacent hole, straight across the rife and down another hole as if on elastic. The collie put his nose down a hole and indicated that there were loads of rabbits down there, probably as many as thirty. Out popped a rabbit at my side, and the fawn bitch caught it. Then another bolted, which the collie herded neatly into the lurcher's jaws. Suddenly we didn't feel so fed up any more.

There followed as lovely a display as you could wish of dogs having their mouths over the right holes and scooping up bolting rabbits, the collie turning escapees just right for the fawn bitch to course and catch. The lad, oblivious to this magical example of ferreting dogs at their best, announced that it was his dinner time and he was going home. We had no time to get lonely without him as along came a man walking his dog on the side that wasn't our permission, and he called across to us about the thirty rabbits he always sees there. Despite our little chat with him, we still managed to bolt and catch fourteen rabbits out of our side of that bank, and decided to pack up when both ferrets came out. The hill was a lot better going down than up, and we avoided the gates this time by going through a fairly obvious gap that for some reason the boy had not shown us on the way up.

Calling in at the farm to say our thank-yous and we'll be off nows, we realised that our pleasure at catching twenty-two rabbits was not impressing anyone, and several voices told us that there were still at least a dozen rabbits on the blackthorn bank last time anybody looked, which was about half an hour ago now. We said our goodbyes aware of the disappointment we had caused, and as we started packing the gear away in the cars, an old boy approached us for the express purpose of telling us that there had been at least thirty rabbits out in the field that very morning. The fawn bitch growled at him very softly, and I stifled a strong desire to giggle. Funnily enough, we've never been asked to go back there, and there is every chance, in my opinion, that there might still be thirty rabbits on the land.

Thirteen

Snow Business

IDON'T know if many working lurchers have stayed at the Hilton, but one of mine did, years ago, and on expenses, too. At the time, I worked at a major international airport, and had an unusual array of responsibilities. One morning, the Chief of all Chiefs called me to the Inner Sanctum and explained that we had blizzards forecast, which meant he and I were staying on-site, covering the days and nights and keeping the show on the road until the weather improved. Rank hath its privileges, so he would be doing the days and I the nights, twelve hours on duty each time. Mercifully, he owned dogs and understood the predicament this would put me in, as I lived alone then. "Go home right now" he said, "and get your dog".

Dog duly got and the weather snapping at my heels even as I drove back up the motorway, I discovered we had been booked into the Hilton. Hotels of such standing do not bat an eyelid at a lurcher staying, and she, regal as all her ilk, did not bat one either, accepting the rise in living standards as her due, or come to that, long overdue. Thank goodness she was a house dog, and had impeccable manners, staying quietly in the room while I went about my work at night, picking her way daintily along the snow-covered grass landside of the

deserted cargo sheds when I took her for her ablutions, and enjoying her share of my breakfast and lunch when I returned to the room to sleep. I could not take her into the airside areas with me when I was working, as that was technically "international" and she would have had to have gone into six months' quarantine afterwards, so she had a fair spell left on her own in the room, but she was good as gold. I did try her in my office, but although she was useful as a paper-shredder, she barked at people going past, and as everyone was rather tired and edgy, I thought it best not to push my luck. My Guv'nor was already attracting criticism for allowing her to stay with me, but bless his cotton socks, he stood his ground.

As the Office Wallahs doing the complaining were showing no inclination to get out there in the weather, leading the troops, they didn't attract a lot in the way of respect from any of us.

We managed for three nights, but the Hilton was fully booked for the fourth, and so the lesser hotel on the airport was asked to accommodate us instead. Enter a Jobsworth hotel manager, who said that they would only take a "small" dog. I explained that she was a small dog on long legs (this was pushing credibility a bit as she was a Deerhound cross). Jobsworth refused to take her. The Chief said words to the effect that the hotel would take the dog, and Jobsworth,

roused, said that they would not. I never asked precisely what followed, but dog and I moved in that afternoon, to a swathe of hastily made-up rules such as "it" must not go into any of the public areas or make a noise or get on the bed.

Our two days at that hotel were punctuated by unruly children and noisy guests, but my lurcher and I lived in our room in discreet silence, our vengeance being the enjoyment of sharing vast breakfasts and afternoon grills on room service, cosied up together on the double bed.

Fourteen

The Mad Beggars

"**I**CAN'T believe you mad beggars are going to ferret this", said the Sahib as I did my pre-ferreting recce. Certainly no other mad beggars had ferreted it in as long as either of us could remember. One local man would pick at the easy buries once or twice a winter, and several of us shot the fields at night, but ferret this? Never.

It was huge even by Sussex standards, running the entire length of a big field, and with the remains of a concrete track along one side (that's where we get the lie-up, then). Once, there had been a hedge, but now just isolated fallen trees and straggled hawthorn and blackthorn showed, with the odd stunted elder. Lots of roots – that's where we get the lie-up too. A cold winter for this part of the country had killed off the nettle crop that normally swathed the bury, but small, spicy nettles were already glinting through the roots, and it would be un-ferretable in another couple of weeks. Three of us turned out to sack this monstrous bury, with three dogs, a dozen ferrets and every net we could muster, including those horrible thin nylon ones that you can never quite bring yourself to give away.

You couldn't long-net this, because the rabbits would bolt along the hedgeline, plopping out of one hole and straight

back into another, so we purse-netted the outer holes, the more open ones and the likely-looking ones, because we were looking at around a quarter of a mile of interconnecting bury, and each hundred yards swallowed every net we possessed, some three hundred between us at that time. Therefore we aimed to collect the ferrets at a suitable point, pick up the nets behind us and reset in front, to get the best out of our firepower. Out in the field were buries that looked isolated but in fact connected with this vast coney conurbation. We left these, considering that the rabbits would be unlikely to bolt from them, which proved to be correct.

I am not generally a fan of working several dogs together ferreting, as it tends to bring out the worst in the jealous ones, cow the shy ones and ruin the retrieving, but in this case, the dogs were so different that it could work. One looked like a Labrador mongrel – which you could say she was – but if you let your gaze linger, you saw rather a deep chest and a very long tail. This dog was inexperienced as a ferreter, but biddable, steady, and with a superb nose. Her colleague was a Bearded collie cross, very experienced and with all the intelligence you would expect, but again, not a dog to attract attention in the casual observer. The third was my young bitch, looking exactly what she was: a fast, typey lurcher. These three often worked together as part of a bobbery pack, but this was the first time they had been brought together for ferreting. The Labrador cross was everybody's friend, but

Photo: Fay Sechiari.

the other two were both feisty bitches, and eyed each other warily.

You don't use any old ferrets for a job like this either. Given that it was almost spring and the jills were on the edge of coming into season, we needed ferrets that were used to each other and would concentrate on the job in hand rather than squaring up to strangers. Luckily, one of us breeds working ferrets from well-tested stock, and he had brought twelve sandy jills. Between us we raised a dozen locator collars, which we fitted to our wriggling army once we finished netting. It took well over an hour to net a hundred yards, and we were losing the will to live by the time we were ready to enter the ferrets. The upside was that we didn't need to let the bury settle because the finish was such a long way from the start. A quick swig of tea, and we were ready to see what the rabbits would make of us.

Sandy buries go deep, and you rarely hear that warning thundering of ferrets and rabbits making contact that you get with harder soil. Our first rabbit pinged out into a net to be held by the nearest dog, and then a second broke from an un-netted hole, saw the reception party, and bolted into a netted hole: just what we had hoped would happen. Rabbits were backnetted, coursed and caught, pinned by a dog in the mouth of the bury, or snapped up in mid-air. The three dogs working together could put enough pressure on an unnetted rabbit to push it out in the open, where the fastest dog could course it and the two slower ones would flank her a length behind and keep the rabbit from turning. There were so many ferrets that the rabbits didn't have a chance of stopping up or hiding in the deepest parts of the bury, and out they shot like champagne corks. We stumbled across the bury in that strange open-armed Ferreters' Waddle, occasionally sinking to the ankles where the sand gave way, and exploring the stinging properties of those tiny nettles as we necked and re-netted as fast as we could. When we came to a natural lull, we gathered up the ferrets, and set the nets forward.

We didn't have one single lie-up except briefly under the concrete track (where else?) where the Labrador lurcher marked the ferret for us and tried to trench along to her. Thankfully this caused the jill to come out by herself. Evidently, so much ferretage moves the rabbits along too fast to cause lie-ups, and when the ferrets flushed a nest of squeakers, they dealt

with them quickly and kept moving. Rabbits breed all year round here in the south, but winter young have a low survival rate.

I was exhausted by the end of the day: thank goodness my colleagues were younger and tougher. It took an hour and a half to pick up all the nets and paunch out the rabbits, by which time the air had that going-home chill to it. The Mad Beggars Formation Ferreting Team will be ready to tackle this bury earlier next season, because now we have the knack of it, and there are two similar to be tried in the adjacent fields.

Fifteen

On Foot and Horseback

BY courtesy of many horses wildly varying in temperament and ability, I have had memorable times riding to hounds. To ride rather than hunt was certainly my intention to begin with, but half a second after the first burst of hound music I was hooked, and have been a hopeless, happy addict ever since. Of necessity, my hunting was maintained on a shoestring budget, and so my four-legged conveyances sometimes were not the ideal choice for the task. Or for any task, in a few cases.

Other people's horses were mostly on offer for some sinister reason, possibly my favourite comment of them all being "You won't mind if he drops dead?" alluding to a seventeen-year-old ex-racehorse that had never really come to terms with being off the track. I hunted him for two seasons that were exhilarating and terrifying by turns, and the old devil didn't hand in his keys until he was past thirty.

Acquiring my own horse brought new dimensions to the sport. I had developed a real taste for Thoroughbreds by then, and my tiny bay blood weed had no brakes, no steering, no sense, jumped like a stag and received admiring comments for it, and gave me six unforgettable seasons. I still remember one particular hedge and ditch, where I seemed airborne for a

very long time before floating back to earth, and found upon landing that only three of us had jumped it. The other two comprised one of the Master's sons, and a friend of mine, sweet sixteen at the time, who had the most angelic blonde blue-eyed looks, a stonking great bay horse, and a command of English more suited to a stevedore. "Did you see that something great ditch?" she lisped.

"If I'd known about that something great ditch, I'd never have jumped it", I replied with feeling. The Master's son, a teenager as well (I was an old lady of thirty) blushed crimson. Later we went to look at the jump on foot, and my word it was indeed a something great ditch. The hedge was over five foot high and very wide as well.

Like the horse from Devizes, mine had legs of all different sizes, and the vet once suggested breaking him down for spares. When finally my nerve, my back and his legs had reached the same parlous state, we agreed to retire together, and we both missed hunting tremendously. Not every horse can corner like a motorbike and regularly bring you home with turf on your stirrup iron; I've never been a brave rider but on a horse of that calibre, you really have no choice.

During my time of active service, I considered footfollowers very nice if rather mysterious people. Footies would kindly open gates, put rails back up, and tell me which way everyone had gone. Those times were many, when I had been left behind trying to lift a sagging gate out of twelve inches of slurry and

tie it shut with an elderly piece of frayed binder band that was just too short, while trying to retain my grip on half a ton of horse that wanted to be somewhere else by yesterday. They would even leg me back up on a horse I never wanted to see in my life again, which happened quite a few times while I was qualifying point-to-pointers. Whenever and however I arrived in the wake of the action, footfollowers would already be there, silent as the landscape, leaning on their sticks and smiling, seeing it all happen. What is more, I doubt they ever gave a moment's thought to my method of arrival either. Arms pulled until my shoulders were a solid yoke of pain, hanging off the horse's side like an Apache (sometimes deliberately to avoid low branches, and sometimes not at all intentionally) congratulating myself on the safe negotiation of a particularly unwelcoming fence out of deep mud into deep plough, and then being overtaken by a minute spaghetti-legged child at stirrup level, on a circular shaggy pony that had neatly popped the same place, or even the time I bottled out of jumping a metal gate and ended up jumping an even bigger one, all were moments in time. I might be galloping over grass now and looking as if I was having fun, but by golly I had earned it. And there, standing quietly, were the footfollowers, wondering what the devil had taken us so long.

I had a strange introduction to footfollowing. After I had given up riding my own, I was asked to qualify a farmer's horse one time when her usual rider was hors de combat. I was not doing too good a job of it, as it was a lairy beast and far too strong for me. It was one of those hunting days where you do your best to stay at the back out of the way, and somehow the field shakes itself and there you are at the front. I needed to stay at the back because this horse didn't seem to like having more than two feet on the ground at any one time; at one stage a lady galloping behind me saw the swishing tail and raised back, and called in mellifluous tones, "I say, is your horse likely to kick?" to which I answered, while hanging on like grim death, "No Madam, he's going to buck" and he ruddy well did too. I was hanging on so tightly that you couldn't have got a fag paper between me and the saddle, but he didn't half shake me about even so. After a couple of hours, he decided rearing would make a change, so he went up a couple of times to see how I felt about it, and then lost his footing and slid over sideways while I stepped gracefully off. A kind footie offered to help me back on, although I really wasn't too sure that it was a good idea, and having got back up there, I thought I had better quit while I was ahead and hack back to the farm before the horse killed me. Having done that, I cleaned the horse up, made him comfortable, thatched under his rug with straw because that was what you did in those days (modern rugs are so much better) and prepared myself for the mother of all rockets from the farmer.

Instead, she took me into the farmhouse, poured me a massive gin and tonic, and then another, by which time (I'd had no breakfast) I was feeling no pain. Then she shovelled me into the old farm van and took me following the hunt, and it was the most amazing fun. I had never before realised that car-following was such an art. We would hammer along the lanes until I was totally lost, screech to a halt and turn the engine off, and never waited longer than ten minutes for a fox to cross in front of us. Having seen the mounted field away, off we would go again. Sometimes we would park up and take a walk, and behold! There we would be in exactly the right place far more often than not, and if we had not quite anticipated the fox's route correctly (I swear that she had consulted them beforehand) we would be up and away to get it right the next time. We car-followed together for years, until she sold the farm, retired and moved away when well into her seventies, and it remains a rich source of memories, some better looked back on than gone through, as she was nearly as frightening behind a wheel as her horses were under saddle. I had many a white-knuckle ride in that old farm van, sometimes across places that you'd hesitate to take a tractor, but we always got where we were going, and almost always saw the fox and the field on their way.

There are strong, fit, not necessarily young footfollowers who run all day after hounds, and seem considerably less bushed and untidy than I ever was at the end of a day on

horseback, where all I had to do was steer and keep both of us upright. There are those who take their quiet routes walking, and are still there to see the fox cross over in the same place that generations of foxes have crossed over. Taken kindly under their wings, I have seen just as much of a different side of hunting, having the time and distance to watch hounds and huntsman unravel the mystery of the fox's passing. As I formerly exulted in the cross-country gallop on a 'fine lepper', mind pulsing like a computer (speed, terrain, direction, obstacles and capability plus random hazards - 'ware wire, tarmacadam, seeds, loose horse, terrifying bridges) I then much more discreetly and seeking invisibility progressed to seeing Charlie on his way, taking many horsepower where I once took one, and going across to almost bisect the line where I once followed wherever it led. The 'glorious uncertainty' was still there: the 'five and twenty percent of the danger' much reduced.

It was a good time.

Sixteen

Charge of the Light Brigade

LET'S hear it for the Light Brigade. Time was, pied and white lurchers were culled at birth, for there was little hope of homing them. Even if your work was wholly legitimate, there would be occasions where discretion mattered, and a bright white dog coursing a bright russet something across a bright green field might attract the wrong kind of attention. For night work, the old lurchermen claimed that rabbits would see a white dog earlier, and so run for cover, though I submit that several hundred thousand candlepower of light might also give them an inkling that all was not well. In truth, a black dog shows up just as well as a white one, but you can't always let fact get in the way of a good prejudice.

In old legend, the "greyhound" (a term covering rough and smooth running dogs) of the heroes was white with red ears, a colour that still comes through today. Then, a dog that showed up over a long distance was a blessing, for you could not only enjoy watching the course, you could find and enjoy the result afterwards, supposing it was something too big to retrieve. Then along came the invaders with their cockamamie ideas about Game Laws, and it is a triumph of genetics that, after around a thousand years of circumspection in the field for the non-aristocracy, the white and pied dogs still exist. And now

we see more of them, from the flashy socks-and-blaze types, bright as gypsy ponies, to the stark white with or without red ears (look closely, for the red often fades to pale fawn) and in between, every kind of pied. Recently, somebody breeding their first lurcher litter described the pups as "They're all white with big spots, and some of the spots have got stripes", which I thought was rather a nice way of saying brindle pied.

I worked a white bitch for years. She was not my dog, though of my breeding, and she was tremendous on all quarry

before retiring to become a lady's pet. Her colour was certainly no handicap, and as one of her jobs was patrolling flocks of sheep against foxes, there were times when it made a good disguise. Seeing her flickering through the hedgerows before putting on a spurt and then night-night foxy, never lost its magic for me.

Some time ago, one of my friends fielded a brace of white lurchers and a cream merle, and one day, well before the ban, was coming back in the dusk when the merle picked up hot drag, dropped her head and forged on forward, while the white lurchers, both youngsters, ran the heel line as inexperienced dogs often will. While they were thus engaged, the cream dog pushed a fox out from behind a blade of grass, coursed and killed it in a matter of yards, and the sapling dogs realised their mistake and ran back to join the worry. Being lurchers, this didn't take long, but by then night was setting in and curls of mist were gathering, so he set off for home at a hound jog, the lurchers keeping easy pace. There had been recent trouble on the land with undesirables causing damage and leaving litter, and as he approached the last field, he could hear voices and see light from a torch. The dogs ran ahead in reverse pickaxe formation, the merle in the lead, and the trespassers were suddenly confronted by three silent pale

dogs, eyes a-glow, blood on their faces, cantering soundlessly out of the thickening mist.

They may or may not have seen the hooded man all in black loping behind the dogs. There was bloodcurdling screaming, the sound of running feet, and quite possibly a nasty smell. They dropped their torch as well.

Seventeen

Geriatric Ferreting

IT was a day out ferreting for the old and infirm, the Sahib and one ferret being the only healthy participants. The rest of the team comprised an extremely elderly ferret, an even more ancient lurcher, and a friend of ours to whom seventy was a distant memory. I had been laid up for months, and, while I could now walk again, my right arm would never be up to much, so I was of limited use in a ferreting context.

The retired ferret had been brought out of mothballs because a couple of the younger ones were hors de combat after a particularly lively ferreting session two days previously, which had also left the working lurcher in need of time off. We therefore blew the dust off the fifteen-year-old, who was one helluva working dog in her day but understandably had for the last couple of years been representing the team on a consultancy basis only. As for our friend, he loved an occasional day out ferreting, though we suspected more in retrospect than at the time. Like many old farm boy types, he didn't agree with having a dog about the buries, and he could be a bit rough handling the ferrets as he always expected to be bitten, so we had to be a tad careful about what we gave him to do. He could set a good net, but we used to take the netted rabbits from him and administer the coup de gras for him whenever we could, as he favoured the rabbit-punch method and it didn't work all that well. But he was good company, never complained about work or weather, and had some interesting tales to tell. The other ferret was our trusty poley jill, who was raring to go even though she had been a key participant in the previous session. She never seemed to tire, and was a real asset whatever ground we worked.

Although I was fairly mobile, I was somewhat restricted in what I could wear, so was dressed like a refugee from the Oklahoma Land Rush, in a long denim dress and rubber boots. You will be relieved to know that there is no photographic record of this. It did remind me of the days when I would come back in the early hours from the Hunt Ball, call in on the horse and see to his morning chores while wearing a ball gown tucked into my wellies. There is no photographic record of this either, although there was the time - but back to the ferreting.

We arrived at the farm, had a quick chat with the farmer who assured us that there were hundreds of rabbits, and then made our way over the fields and started netting up, watched with great interest by sixty or so sheep. The old lurcher, the sheep and I checked out other buries while the menfolk cleared and netted up the first two sets. It occurred to me that the old dog had not been ferreting for some four years, nearly half a lurcher's working lifetime, so it was not surprising that she was hesitant with her marking. We did not know whether we could trust her lack of interest or not, but it turned out that the first two buries, which she had not marked, were empty, though showing every sign of use. The only other bury in that field was so big and covered with brambles that it was beyond our puny resources, so we went into the next field and made the acquaintance of even more affable sheep, tried another bury which the old trout did mark, albeit reluctantly, and after considerable effort obtained two rabbits. The elderly ferret then decided she'd done her bit and went to sleep, so she was boxed up for the rest of the day. The elderly man reminisced about the huge hauls of rabbits he used to get when but a lad, with one ferret and half a dozen nets. Ah,

82

those were the days. He could hardly ride his bicycle back with all those rabbits festooned across it.

The following bury, which luckily we could drive to, attracted the help of some very friendly calves, which frightened the wits out of the lurcher, pulled the nets about, and tried to eat the two rabbits along with our windscreen wipers. We left in haste and disarray (we hadn't known they were in that field) but not before rediscovering just how far it is possible to slide on one foot in a new cowpat. The next bury, just across the fence, saw the lurcher give her first very decisive mark. Out of that, we got four rabbits out of six; it was so nearly five, but the old dog doesn't have the speed she once did, and got a bit flustered. She then had to have a little lie-down and gather her wits while the calves watched us from over the fence.

Lunch cheered the lurcher up no end. We don't usually lunch on a ferreting trip, preferring to crack on and make the best of the daylight, so this was a bonus. We had first netted

an enormous bury, so we left it to rest and enjoyed some sandwiches and tea (there is no end to the Sahib's talents). The lurcher delicately accepted bits of crust and licked out our crisp bags; thus fortified, she put out a rabbit from a tuft of grass and chased it. She put a few bends in it too, before it made it to the safety of the boundary fence. That was our most productive bury: six out of eight, and very nearly a squashed dog, as she stalled in front of me just as I lunged after a rabbit and tripped over my hem. Take it from me, boys, do not go ferreting in a skirt unless you really have to!

The dog then marked skywards, and we watched in mounting horror as a hot-air balloon floated towards us, rapidly losing height and showing every sign of putting down in one of the fields. Luckily they fired up the burners after getting uncomfortably close, probably having seen the livestock. The lads then tried one more bury, while the dog and I rested in the car, both having exceeded our energy limits. That produced two more rabbits, plus one which escaped, so we decided to end on that note and return the old and sick to their various homes. The lurcher slept so deeply huddled up against me on the way back that I had to keep checking she was breathing. She didn't move much all night, for that matter.

the high-rise rats that used the beams and rafters as their thoroughfares, peeping at us from behind various immovable pieces of farm equipment. The dust settled again into the sheets of cobwebs, giving a Hammer Films effect.

The Sahib, bearing his trusty airgun, was Huntsman, the farmer as Master was entrusted with a good torch, the hound pack consisted of the farm lurcher, and I served as both Whipper-in and Field, my job being to rat-spot, make encouraging noises, and holloa the odd rat away. These rats were used to noise and sudden lights, the granary being worked in at all sorts of odd times, and the comings and goings of people and dogs had never up until now caused them much in the way of disturbance, wild rats having a short life and a merry one, and being fortunate to survive much past their first year. Rat-lamping is a much underrated sport, and only works with rats that have never been disturbed before, because they are clever creatures and learn very fast. These did not have a chance to become lamp-shy as the farmer was accurate with directing the torch-beam only on the hunted rat, the Sahib is a good shot, and the range was tolerably close. In lieu of the music of the pack, we had the screeches and yodels of an excited lurcher to whom silent hunting was an unknown trait; it just seemed to confuse the rats more, and it scrambled my brains a bit as well when heard in an enclosed space. A satisfying number of rats were isolated in the torchlight one by one and then dropped off their perches, and then the Huntsman started to tackle some rickety old ladders. "You wouldn't have gone up that if you'd seen it in daylight", I said as he leaned over at disc-slipping angles to shoot rats that were crammed into those small spaces between friendly wooden uprights, doors and walls, lintels and gaps. Then he was off up an external wooden staircase that was older than the farmhouse, to shoot at peering whiskery faces along a floor that showed light and dark like piano keys, or on top of long-defunct containers. There was one occasion when a rat showed at a gap so close to the gun that I thought it was going to snatch it away and shoot back, and another one caused the entire Hunt to duck and dive in disarray by leaping over the Master's shoulder. Luckily, the lurcher was in exactly the right place to catch it in the air and give it a good shaking, after which it was no threat to anybody. When a succession of rats abandoned their posts to stream past him, he would crunch and drop and get to the next faster than we could see, but individual rats were always given a shaking as well, especially if he had worked up a head of steam by having to wait for one.

This dog was a superb 'finder' for even in all the dust and rat-smell, he would fix on any place a rat was concealed and stare at it until one of us could come along and dislodge it. We moved to tackle the outside walls, and he was right there, standing on his hindlegs to mark rats above his head. This wasn't, you understand, the discreet marking of a highly-trained ferreting lurcher, but the demented screaming of a

very loud one (ever heard whippets waiting to race? That kind of loud, only louder) and no prizes for guessing why such a handsome dog had been found in rescue kennels. It just goes to show how one person's reject can be another's prize, for it meant nothing to the farmer that his dog made a noise, and as for us, well, we just thought he was trying to be equal to an entire pack of hounds.

Afterwards, the pack sat on the Huntsman's lap, or as much of it as he could fit on, the rest overflowing comfortably onto an elderly leather sofa, while the Master dispensed tea, cake and whisky. We weren't sure about the final tally, but agreed it was "the best part of a tidy few". I can thoroughly recommend rat-lamping; it's a much underrated and very effective fieldsport.

Nineteen

Deer, Stoats
and Ferreting

WE were ferreting ahead of the 'myxy', which had already been seen on the far edges of the estate, where it normally starts. The bracken had been cut, which made our job a lot easier, and the new nettle growth was only averagely painful. The Colly prowled about marking occupied buries and giving us that feral "Get on with it" look from under her brows. By the time we had netted four buries, taking every net I possessed, which is rather a lot these days, she was getting distinctly antsy with us. Three weeks into her pregnancy and still razor-lean, she would still have been able to run escapees, but I did not want her to do too much, so I was being extra careful with my net-setting. She escorted us back to the ferret boxes, nudging us to hurry up. Nothing like knowing who is in charge.

As soon as the ferrets went down, Ms Impatience was all ice cool control. She froze in that classic stance, only her ears and eyes moving, only the lift of the tip of her tail telling us if something was about to happen. These sandy buries run deep, and it can take ferrets a while to drive the rabbits up from their lowest levels. Occasionally you can hear the rumbling down below as the ferrets make contact, but more usually the first you know of it is the puff of sand and the net

at the end of its drawcord, with the dog pinning the contents until one of us arrives to deal with it. Today, the rabbits had the decency to bolt in ones and twos, so that there was no hasty dashing about trying to despatch rabbits, reset nets and arrest ferrets in multiples. We worked steadily across the first bury, hearing the keening of buzzards overhead: it was a clear day and good to be out.

Around a fold in the high ground came a fallow pricket, bouncing along with his tail up. He came quite close to us and stood goggling, then did what the Sahib calls "that damnfool gerboingy thing" on the spot, a suicidal invitation to any predator. The Colly looked, looked away, and concentrated on the bury. Those are Leave-Its, she said. He didn't seem in any hurry to go, even when I suggested he might, using a pithy lowland phrase, but eventually he bounded off, all the way down the valley, in no great hurry at all. I never understand why deerstalkers go to all that trouble; you only have to be out with a lurcher doing something law-abiding, and the ruddy things throw themselves at you. He would have been nice tender eating, too, but I quelled that thought and carried on with the ferreting.

Those four buries got us off to a good start, and the Sahib went on with the dog to check out some more buries while I picked up nets and then started on the fifth in the row. I had just gone back for more nets when I saw a stoat travelling down from the release pen towards the partly-netted bury. He was bright russet in the autumn sun, moving at a lively bounce, not a care in the world until he reached the bury and saw the nets. He fluffed up and ticked in annoyance like a ferret, bounced himself in a few sideways circles and then went down an un-netted hole into the bury. Many's the time I have bolted a stoat while ferreting, but I have never entered ferrets in a bury while knowing a stoat was down there. I wondered what would happen: would the ferrets bolt the stoat, would the stoat bolt some rabbits, would rabbits, ferrets and stoat be doing some sort of Benny Hill chase round and round the bury? We put four ferrets in and waited to find out.

What happened was about twenty minutes of nothing, just long enough to make us think we shouldn't have done that, and then rabbits firing out of the bury in all directions. We were all hands to the pumps, and when the action stopped, we had a tidy pile of rabbits. We never did see the stoat again, but one of the ferrets came up with evidence of having killed a rabbit, so maybe the stoat was dining below.

By then, the large bury that the Sahib had netted on his own had had time to settle, so we moved our equipment across, upsetting a vast fallow buck that had been lying still under a bracken frond through all the previous disturbance. For a moment the sky went dark and then he was away, leaving the rank smell of one soon to be in rut. The dog had returned to heel and was looking up at me with unfathomable eyes: maybe she wanted me to acknowledge her good behaviour, or maybe the shades of her Grandma and Great-Grandma were whispering in her ears. Once upon a time, deer work had been legal, and our contribution welcomed, but what was good for previous generations of lurchers no longer applied, no matter what was in their genes. So we wasted no time in putting ferrets to ground and had a textbook threequarters of an hour of bolting rabbits into purse-nets, and occasionally out of them again, though we did not actually lose any thanks to the dog. Because of her condition, I would not be taking her out working again until the New Year, so the day was especially good. This is one place where we could leave the paunch for the buzzards, so we cleaned out a catch that was far larger than either of us had expected, and just what the butcher had wanted.

Twenty

Tis the Season

NO matter how much you might want to appear normal on at least one day of the year, Christmas with animals, and especially lurchers, tends to ruin the effect. I remember the year I was invited out for Christmas lunch, and JB the Deerhound cross was five months old, sassy as they come. The little moo was going through a running-away phase, and believe me, she had no respect for anything: I had to rewrite the textbook for that hound. I had tried driving off and leaving her, but she wasn't bothered.

Nothing fazed her, nothing motivated her, and it took me uppermost of a year before we came together as a team. She became a tremendous and most loyal working dog, but that was a long time in the future, and what I had then was a big predatory sapling loose on a large commercial shoot. My friendship with the 'keeper was still in the future, too: I had to catch my dog before he did. I had to walk her down.

I've done this with horses. You follow just close enough to keep the animal on the move, not threatening, not talking, not making eye contact or attempting to catch, just not letting it stop for a moment. It can take varying amounts of time – think hours here – but once the animal capitulates, you have made great strides in your relationship. The pup walked and

I walked and we went a long way. It was a couple of hours before she turned, and I crouched down with arms open and head turned away. She ran into my arms trembling, and she licked the tears off my face. I missed my Christmas lunch, but that was a great Christmas.

Then there was the year I was out riding at first light with The Worm at heel, and we saw a strange heap on the road. As we approached, it turned into a peacock, uttered a maiden-auntly scream and took off. Flying about four feet off the ground, it was perfect for a young running-dog to race after, teeth clicking at the zenith of each leap, trying to grasp that flowing train of feathers. "You catch it – I'll cook it" had long been our motto, and it was a somewhat tail-challenged peacock that finally flew over a wall to safety. Mind you, I don't know what the horse would have done, as he could be mighty sniffy about dead bodies slung across the saddle, and more than once I'd had to walk home leading him as the beggar

Snapping back into the present, and satisfied that the Rottie was out of the equation, I escorted the Vizsla back to the boundary fence at warp factor eight (not bad for my age), while telling it loudly to go away. The Sahib informs me that I was using a most unladylike turn of phrase, which will no doubt come as much of a surprise to you as it did to me: I'm sure he must have misheard.

Once the Rottie stopped windmilling like a beetle on its back, it was off back to the fence as well, and the Colly, metaphorically dusting her palms, returned to ferreting mode. After all that kerfuffle, the new ferret took a bit of persuading to come out, and we had to give the rabbit best because it certainly wasn't going to bolt now, so we took a command decision to pack up and move on. My Colly resumed her normal shy demeanour, but she hasn't got me fooled any more, because long ago I remember an apologetic, introverted little bitch surprisingly like her, who never in all her life turned her head at any quarry.

Twenty-two

Garden Rabbits

THIS is the time of year when people who have ignored you for months become friendly. That is because they have rabbits in their gardens. Even though you told them last year (and the year before) that high summer is not the time you can do much useful in the way of rabbiting, they are adamant that there have been no rabbits until now.

Oh, except for the sweet little baby one (one??) that they found in the woodpile. These are the people you told to get their gardens rabbit-fenced, only they thought it would spoil the view, or they had it done but on the cheap, so that laughing rabbits are pinging over and tunnelling under without hindrance. These are the people who drive out leaving the ruddy gates open, so that rabbits can make their unhurried way from the surrounding fields into the gardens without negotiating the fence at all. You have tried to get them to use a professional Pester, but unfortunately they have heard about the good jobs you did for Mr X and Mrs Y, both of whom have proper rabbit fencing and make getting to grips with the resident lagomorphs easy for you. Both Mr X and Mrs Y are sporting types, and don't mind the carnage that two lurchers can create in formal gardens when in pursuit of coney; also they don't have cats, dogs or children, so you can set traps.

The gardener is a nice chap, and he has been sent to persuade you. What is more, he is offering money, and you are easily bought. You ask if the rabbits are coming in from outside, and he assures you they are not. You ask about the rabbit fencing, and he says they can't get through it, except where they have. He offers the opinion that unless rabbits are living in next-door's garden (and how likely is that?), he cannot see that they are coming in from there. Right then, they must have been beamed down from the Mothership, and those long things they have at the sides of their heads, they'd be antennae. Come to think of it, there have been bright lights over that part of the village some nights.

Having run out of excuses, you take two lurchers and go for a recce. You have to pick a time when the children are at school, assure the gardener that the dogs won't even look at the cat, and meet him by the tradesman's entrance because he has the key and they won't let you have one. The dogs are noses-down immediately, there are rabbit runs, scrapes and droppings on the lawn, and mindful of a reputation to keep up, they flush a rabbit from the shrubbery. There is a great crashing and spraying of tender foliage, and you hold your breath waiting for the yelp, but luckily the gods are with you and they pin the rabbit by the conservatory. As you are

necking it, you look up to see a small sprog watching you out of the window. Oopsie.

Leaving the rabbit by the edge of the lawn to collect later, you check out the wilder part of the garden and find a blessed great badger sett. It seems disused, but there are laws about this sort of thing and no, you won't be ferreting it. The gardener thinks it is where the rabbits are living. You explain about traps and the regular visiting of, and you are assured that the family is going on holiday shortly, and could you trap the rabbits while they are away? They cannot let you have a key to the garden door, but the gardener is so keen to get rid of the pesky fluffies that he will meet you every day and let you in. Damn.

Coming back into the formal garden, you see a small cortege of children carrying the recently deceased rabbit in a box. There is a bunch of flowers in every chubby fist, and Nanny is digging a hole under the apple tree.

Twenty-three

Early Days

SHE caught her first rabbit, and I wasn't there. It's like missing Baby's first steps. I have always been there before to see the first rabbit, the first rat, and in happier times, the first of other creatures too. None of my dogs has caught a rabbit as the first success, not unless you count one that was so rancid with 'mixy' that it could barely hop, which the Black Death picked up when she was a mere eighteen weeks old. But I missed the first proper rabbit caught on the run with a spectacular strike and somersault. The Sahib was there, and I was not. Damn.

Most of the other puppy owners have kept in touch, and we compared notes as they developed. I knew these pups were going to be serious weapons, and I had to be very careful where they went. I told everyone to keep the handbrake on and not let them start catching too soon, because if the prey drive kicks in before the obedience is established, brother, you will reap the whirlwind. Even with our collective best efforts, we couldn't keep them from their vocation for long enough, and reports filtered in of little accidents, such as one leaping into the lower branches of a tree after a squirrel while still on the lead, causing a sudden attack of Tourette's from the other end of the lead, in front of shocked mummies and

traumatised children in the park. The Black Death caught
a squirrel when she was five months old, but let it go when
it made a loud noise and luckily before it bit her. Avian life

better organised; with a few, the first rabbit is hit hard and the subsequent ones caught more gently, but some strike every one as hard as the last.

I have seen dogs run 'gruellers' on hares, doing everything right except striking, which is why quite a few coursing dogs do a season of rabbit work before they progress to hares. Their canny owners know that chasing a quarry that has to be picked or missed in fifty or so yards really gets a dog using its mouth. Once on hares, the dogs have to learn to play a longer game, but they retain the desire to change gear and speed into their quarry when the time is right, and while this is instinctive in some, others have done their homework and learned on rabbits. I have seen dogs bitten by foxes because they tried to pick up without that first sledgehammer hit that knocks the stuffing out of the quarry before it can fight back. If strike is inborn, then these tasks are accomplished so much more neatly. Can training teach a dog to strike? I know lurcher owners who train for it using a lure on a line, and others who say that you can't beat ratting to develop it, but I believe it is an inborn talent and you can't put it there. So where do you look for it? In my experience, there is no single factor, and any cross of lurcher can have it or not. The gentlest, most timid running dog can be just as likely to hit an axe-blow to speeding quarry as a bolder type. The best guide is breeding: if the parents strike then the pups should.

I remember a greyhound coming into retirement out of coursing, and beginning a second career as a fox dog, back in the Seventies when winter pelts were worth a bit. He had never seen a fox or been lamping before, but was a keen dog to pick up a hare as opposed to just chasing it, and his owner thought he might do all right. They went out with an experienced fox man, and before very long, a fox appeared in the beam. Owner and greyhound stood riveted, watching this animal, until the fox man hissed something on the lines of: 'kindly get a move on and slip the dog'. It was an uphill run, and the greyhound was still accelerating as it hit the fox, which fell over, as indeed anyone hit at thirty mph by a seventy-five pound dog would. The greyhound kept going,

over the brow of the hill and into darkness. The fox staggered to its feet, crossed its legs, went down and expired; while the men were looking at it in wonderment, the greyhound came hacking back with another fox in its mouth. That's what you call 'strike'.

Twenty-five

Dog

by Phillip Blackman

THERE must be others out there, I suppose, who suffer from the same affliction as I. Namely a Lakeland terrier. Now in her sixteenth year, she is a trifle doddery, inclining towards more realistic feats of deafness even than in her wild youth, broken toothed, scraggy, scarred (more from incidents involving the other terrier than work) and generally senile, and yet the miserable old faggot, if she finds a hot scent or sees the gun come out, sheds her years in a truly miraculous fashion.

Now, I am no dog trainer (can terriers be trained?) so all of the infuriating old ratbag's talents are self-taught. In her younger days she would sit with me when roost-shooting pigeons, and often her pointed stare would draw my attention to an approaching pigeon I'd not seen. On those occasions that I'd connect, she would run in to retrieve and when in the right mood a good job she made of it too. Of late she has, however, decided that once she's found anything unlucky enough to fly or run into my shot, it's hers, and proceeds to eat as much of it as possible before I can get to her. Recently, on one of our walks with the gun, the two terriers bolted a rabbit. I was so surprised that I'd missed such a simple shot I forgot to fire the second barrel. Leaving cover behind the coney, both dogs

put their noses to the ground and flew in pursuit. The black one I called off, but without a megaphone about my person I stood no chance of stopping the cantankerous old tart and so resigned myself to a long wait. Many years later, tired of waiting, the one comparatively well-behaved dog and I decided to do a circuit of the small field we were in, hunting out the hedges as we went. Twenty minutes or so, two pigeons, one squirrel and a rabbit later, we timed it perfectly to arrive back at our starting place at the same time as the reprehensible old serpent who greeted us by chundering up half a rabbit. I had hit it and she did still retrieve.

As a young dog it took the vile old crone some time to realise that running at high speed round a clump of brambles containing a rabbit wouldn't cause it to become so dizzy watching her that it would stagger out feeling sick, and that she would have to go in to hoik it out, but once this simple lesson penetrated her granite skull she became the most thorough rabbiting dog I've ever had. Even now in her old age she still finds the odd bunny the other dogs have overlooked, although she has developed an irritating habit of baying whilst running heel. Daft old bat that she is.

It was probably in her first year that she encountered the delights of crows, when one I'd only winged bit her. For some time afterwards she'd circle a downed black thing baying like mad until the rancid old witch learnt the knack of getting in quick and crunching them. From then on anything corvid which was shot, was severely worried, and only by rendering her unconscious can it be retrieved from her crocodile jaws. Similarly, her first squirrel was a wounded one, which climbed her front leg and bit her. Nowadays it's a race to get to a shot squirrel before the loathsome old harpy lays claim to it.

As I was not overly keen on my little girl meeting the sort of nasty savage monsters that dwell 'neath the earth and for which she was of course bred to tackle, she was eight before first going to ground, and this during a boiling hot summer afternoon' s pigeon shooting. A keeper friend and myself had set up in a thick hedge; one facing each direction guarding a few decoys each. After a while with not much about, I thought it might be a good idea to find the disreputable old hag who should have been with us. Just a few yards from my hide I nearly fell down the sort of hole which if it only held rabbits I didn't want to meet them. From said hole emanated, as if I needed to tell you, faint canine sounds. The manky old fleabag was baying her head off.

Once my friend had regained his composure, wiped his eyes and started breathing normally again he took the Landrover and fetched digging tools. Have you ever tried digging in sun baked, rock hard clay in the middle of a hedge? Here was ground undisturbed since Adam was a lad. The pick bounced off of it. My accomplice, a man used to digging to terriers, looked worried. "Could you, perhaps, call her off, do you suppose?" he enquired, a tad optimistically. I just looked at him. "No, of course not. Lakeland. Sorry." and we redoubled our efforts. To cut a long story short after much sweat had softened the ground and many blisters had decorated our hands we dug to the disgusting old harridan proudly baying on the most toothless, scrawny, manky

looking old vixen we'd ever seen. Shooting her, the fox that
is, was an act of kindness.

It was when the foul old harlot was about ten I realised that
although apparently in league with the devil, it was unlikely
she was immortal and so Winnie, named after Mrs Mandela
as she shared, even at such an early age, many of the good
lady's traits, joined us. The dear sweet old lady played with
the pup and they were great company for one another, or so
I thought. I doubt if Winnie was a year old before we had
the first fight. Many were to follow. It you have terriers you'll
understand, possibly nodding your head sympathetically.

A few of their full and frank exchanges of views stand out,
such as the occasion when, out for an amble with the gun, we
found a nice flight line across a hay meadow. Soon after me
taking up position in a ditch bottom, the first pigeon fell out of
sight to the left. Both sweet little doggies ran in to retrieve. At
my shot, pigeons started moving all round and I was kept busy
for some while. When eventually there was a lull I found the

dear little things had fought to a standstill, and with tongues a yard long, they were covered in blood but lying together as though the best of friends. Perhaps the most spectacular of their slight disagreements occurred one evening when a young lady of my acquaintance was visiting. My two delightful, cuddly, little bow-wows latched on to each other. I should at this juncture explain that if I ever managed to choke the damned things apart, the little black swine would give in and go limp, the satanic old demon, however, would continue, in a blind fury, to snap and bite anything in reach. This is just what happened on this occasion. My prospective beloved was treated to the sight of me hurling abuse and expletives, which in the cold light of day I blush to recall, while holding up two snarling dervishes by their throats and attempting to choke the life out of them. Eventually they parted, and as they did, the evil old besom spun round and her jaws clamped shut on my belly button. Damn but that hurt! The bruise, I should point out, lasted a lot longer than the romance.

Having passed her decade and a half it has on occasion been pointed out that perhaps I should be thinking about a replacement. Perhaps a proper dog, some rather hurtfully say, a spaniel or Labrador, would suit my purpose better. I've been told that what I really need is a good lurcher to complement Winifred, creating the perfect working team. I've even been offered a Chesapeake Bay. But if the wonderful old darlin' should one dark day need replacing I know just what dog I want. A Lakeland! God help me.

Twenty-six

Missing

by Phillip Blackman

WHAT is it about missing that's so bloody easy? This is a rhetorical question, so there's no need to write in with suggestions. Thank you. I'm one of those silly buggers who have the bad habit of counting the empty cartridges in my pocket at the end of the day. I know what you're thinking. "Oh dear", you're thinking, "this can only lead to deep depression. Don't do it, you bloody fool."

I know, don't think I don't. The Samaritans will no longer accept calls from me. If, using someone else's phone and a disguised voice, I manage to get through I'm told to "Bugger off and kill yerself. We don't care." I think it was them who put my name on Exit's mailing list. They suggested I shoot myself. I knew I'd miss. But enough of this dark gloom and thoughts of taking up golf or some other form of sado-masochism.

I try to put it out of my head, you see, and tell myself it's the sport that counts, they must have been incredibly testing birds and I should be proud of that single teal I've just hung up in the shed prior to emptying twenty-one cartridges into the bin. I can't fool myself though. I know that they were all easy shots hovering over the splash just in front of me. I blush to recall that I even missed a sitter that I fired at in my frustration. And the teal? I can't lie to you; I heard a single

shot over on the neighbour's ground the other side of the river and after a lengthy pause a wing-tipped duck crash-landed in front of me to be nailed by Winnie after a fine course. So there you have it, the plain truth, I confess, this evening I have fired off twenty-one shots and have sweet Fanny Adams to show for it. I could blame the gun. I could blame the cartridges. I could blame the earth for spinning so fast it made me dizzy. That one's not a bad idea actually, I might run with that. Yes that's it: the earth momentarily span faster, so that I should have not only given the birds lead, I should have aimed slightly to the left as well. Who am I kidding? I'm only lying to myself. I should just accept I've had an off day. It happens. It's no big deal. Think of all the times when everything's gone right.

Times when I can do no wrong, times when the pigeons flock to the decoys and at every double shot two, or perhaps even three, more lie on the stubble, times when every bird that is sent over my peg is high and curling until the moment my trigger finger causes its instant demise, times when the rabbits are bolting fast and furious from the ferret only to roll limply down the hill with every shot from my gun, times when the duck briefly seen against the town-glow-lit clouds fall with an almost unsporting regularity. Oh yes, those were the times. I wish I could remember them.

What do I remember? Rabbits, sitting rabbits, looking round mildly surprised at that loud noise, the accusing expression on the ferret's face as it ambles out to see how I've got on, on days when I really should have left the gun at home and netted up instead; the pigeons coming into the decoys in text book fashion, hovering over them, and after a double-barrelled salute, departing; tree-top height pheasants waggling their tails derisively, and as I've already described on the one occasion in the year when we have enough water on the farm to bring the ducks in, all I do is inconvenience them slightly.

There have been days, and I hope there will be again, when bunnies roll head over heels to a well-placed charge of shot, and fowl fall with a satisfying regularity from the sky, but right now I'm in a deep slough of despair. Whilst I think about it, have you ever noticed how easy it is to miss crows? Huge great lumbering things, slowly flapping towards you, plenty of time, then they're there, bang bang, and then they're gone with the minimum of evasive action.

Perhaps I could set up a shooting school for people who find clay-shooting boring, enjoy the thrill of the chase but don't actually want to kill anything, but I'd probably get sued by numerous outraged clients who have inadvertently killed more head of game in one day than Lord Walsingham and Duleep Singh killed between them in their whole lifetimes.

"Relax and take your time. You've got plenty of time." I tell myself and I know it's right because in the past I've been able to listen to myself and relax and take my time and it's worked. I've started hitting things again, but this time I snap at myself, "I know I've got to relax and take my time and, yes,

I know there's plenty of time. So stop nagging me!" and I get tenser, and any semblance of the smoothness of action that is indicative of good shooting goes right out of the window as I poke, and stop the swing, and the only things that fall to the ground are empty cases, and Winnie yawns, curls up and goes to sleep.

Woodcock: I used to think woodcock were a piece of cake, couldn't understand what all the fuss was about. On the rare occasions I'd be invited to shoot where there were a few, every time there'd be that slow-seeming drifting, flicking flight, or fast and high crossing a valley, easy, I couldn't miss. Then what happens? I open my big, fat gob. That's what happens. A couple of years ago I said much the same to a fellow Gun on a woodcock-rich shoot. I haven't hit one of the long-beaked buggers since, that's the birds not fellow Guns. Snipe the same. Many years ago we had a lot of snipe on the farm. Whether they were walked up, zigging and zagging, or coming back over me high and fast in the wind, I couldn't miss. No

problem. Something happened. A few dry years, perhaps, when they didn't turn up, allowing me to get out of practice. Perhaps I'm just getting old and slow. Whatever, snipe are now safe, it seems, when I'm around.

At times I think maybe I should accept the inevitable and just give up shooting, but the trouble is I know what I'm doing wrong and, worse, I know that until that magical day, it might be today, tomorrow, next week, next month even, when I wake up, innocently unaware that this isn't going to be another day devoted to the the cartridge manufacturers' benevolent fund, and just go out there and shoot, and hit what I'm shooting at because something's clicked and I can shoot again, there's nothing I can do about it. When that magical day dawns, however, I could shoot blindfolded, one-handed and standing on one leg and still the tallest pheasants, the twistiest, most evasively jinking pigeon, the fleetingliest seen duck or the fastest rabbit will fall victim to my fowling piece. On such a day the sun will shine, birds will sing, my nearest and dearest will rejoice and somewhere Julie Andrews will be singing.

So consoling myself with the thought of that holy grail of days, a bit like posting the pools coupon, I tear up the latest leaflet from Exit, clean the old gun, pat Winnie and forgo my daily call to the Samaritans.

Twenty-seven

Amen to That

IT came to pass in the days before the celebration of the birth of our Lord, that a man tilling the fields saw a multitude of rabbits thereon. And he summoned us on the mobile horn and spake thus: get thy hinder parts over here soon as thou likest and rid me of these pestilent beasts. And at the same time the women in the households of the village spake with anger and said gettest thou out from under my feet or else do something useful. And so we summoned the beasts of underground hunting, and the long-leggity hounds, and set forth unto the fields. And the children of the households begged to come also, and we said, only if thou art quiet and behave thyselves or verily the wrath of Jackie D will fall upon thee.

And we brought the nets of hemp and the nets of spun nylon and laid them over the places where the rabbits would

Illustration: Edward Andrews

bolt, and verily the holes were many so that we were forced to deploy also the cheapo nets of thin nylon that doth tangle if thou lookest at it. And even the children were set unto this task, and the clearing of the plants of the field that do sting and prickle, and they waxed indignant, and were glared at, for did our Lord not say that little children should suffer? And the largest son wailed and beat his breast and sayeth it was slave labour, and was told to get on with it sharpish.

And one of the dogs did produce an eye-watering amount of ordure, so that we saith among us good grief what do you feed that? And one of our number commenteth that it was enough to turn a tractor over.

And we let forth an army of ferrets such as would be sufficient to overcome the hordes, and among those was the ferret Bloody Norah, which hath great beauty but biteth like a fiend. And they did go under the ground, and sent forth thumpings and squealings, and we heard and were content. And the rabbits came out from under the ground and entangled themselves in the nets of hemp and of nylon, and the thin nylon nets were as much good as a teapot that is of chocolate. And the dogs raced across the land and caught the rabbits that slipped the nets, and some of us fell in the nettles and cried out aloud, and called upon the name of Gordon Bennett. And some of us fell among thorns and rent our raiment, and others of us became mired in foul ground which was nothing to do with the dog, but a passing fox. And one picked up Bloody Norah and said Ow. And the son that was the largest was told not to stand there like a bleedin' lemon but to get over here toot sweet and reset some nets.

And it came to pass that the ferrets came out when there were no more rabbits, and were placed in their chariots, and

Photo: Fay Sechiari.

Bloody Norah bit someone else. And the dogs came up and fawned upon us as we paunched out a great multitude of rabbits, and some of the younger children said ooh except for the ones that said eurr yuk. And we paused for refreshment on the journey back, partaking of strong fluids, and there was much discourse on whose dog did what. And the mobile horn did sound with a voice of trumpets, and the man who tilled the fields said Oy, you've missed some, I've just seen three. And the mobile horns did sound yet again and again, from womenfolk desirous of knowing where the fornicating hades we had got to, for the kinsfolk were arriving even now.

And so we returned to our houses and fed our animals and cleansed our raiment and set our nets out to dry. And we were content, and the hell with the kinsfolk.